First Words
with
Peppa Pig
Level 1

D0491514

Paper Planes

Based on the Peppa Pig TV series

Meet

Peppa

George

Daddy Pig

Mummy Pig

Mr Rabbit

Learn

a   away   can   help

it   make   to   up   we

Read

newspaper

paper planes

paper

3

Daddy Pig is in a rush to go away.
"Can we help?" said Peppa and George.
"I can not find the big plan for
Mr Rabbit," said Daddy Pig.

Peppa and George go to see Mummy Pig.
"Can we make paper planes?" said Peppa.

"You can. You can bend bits of paper into paper planes. I will help," said Mummy Pig.

The paper planes go up and away.
"Can you help us make the next paper plane?"
said Peppa.
"You can make it, Peppa. George can help you.
You can get a bit of paper and bend it," said
Mummy Pig.

"Wheeee!"

Peppa and George go away to find a bit of paper.
They find a big plan.
"This can make the best paper plane," said Peppa.

Daddy Pig is back from his job.
"I did not find the big plan for
Mr Rabbit. Can you help me
find it?" he said.
"Look Daddy, we can make a
paper plane," said Peppa.

14

"I can make it go up and away!" said Daddy Pig.
The paper plane is up, up and away!

The paper plane is here!
Mr Rabbit can see it.